The Joy of Playing for Pleasure

Memorable Themes, Songs, and Pieces for Piano.
Selected and Arranged by Denes Agay.

Yorktown Music Press, Inc.
New York • London • Sydney

Order No. YK 21491
US International Standard Book Number: 0.8256.8075.1
UK International Standard Book Number: 0.7119.1656.X

Exclusive Distributors:
Music Sales Corporation
257 Park Avenue South, New York, New York 10010
Music Sales Limited
8/9 Frith Street, London W1V 5TZ England
Music Sales Pty. Limited
120 Rothschild Street, Rosebery, Sydney, NSW 2018, Australia

Printed and bound in the United States of America by
Vicks Lithograph and Printing Corporation

Table of Contents

Nocturne in Waltz Time

adapted from Op. 9, No. 2

Frederic Chopin
(1810–1849)

Juba Dance

R. Nathaniel Dett
(1882–1943)

D.C. al Fine

Doretta's Song

from "La Rondine"

Giacomo Puccini
(1858–1924)

Serenade melancholique

Peter I. Tchaikovsky
(1840–1893)

Spanish Dance

Playera–Andaluza

Enrique Granados
(1867–1916)

Valse triste

from the music to the drama Kuolema

Jean Sibelius
(1865–1957)

La Plus que lente (Valse)

Excerpt

Claude Debussy
(1862–1918)

Caprice viennois

Fritz Kreisler
(1875–1962)

Polonaise militaire

Frederic Chopin

D.C. al Fine
(without repetition)

Pomp and Circumstance
Land of Hope and Glory

Edward Elgar
(1857–1934)

"Destiny" Waltz

Sydney Baynes

D.C. al Fine

Theme from the "Pathetique" Symphony

Peter I. Tchaikovsky

A Real Slow Drag

theme from the opera Treemonisha

Scott Joplin
(1868–1917)

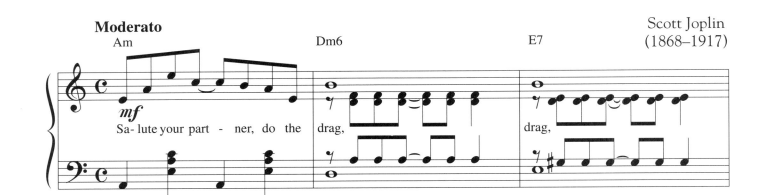

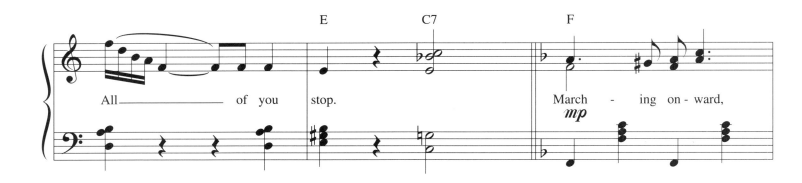

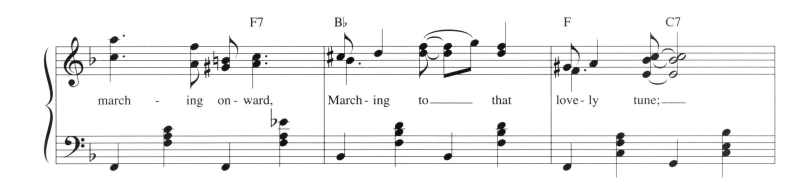

Romance

Anton Rubinstein
(1829–1894)

Theme from Symphony No. 8

Ludwig van Beethoven
(1770–1827)

Allegretto scherzando

Mattinata

Ruggiero Leoncavallo
(1858–1919)

Allegretto from Symphony No. 3

Johannes Brahms
(1833–1897)

Pavane
Theme

Maurice Ravel
(1875–1937)

Clair de lune

from "Suite bergamasque"

Claude Debussy

Song of India

from the opera Sadko

Nikolai Rimsky-Korsakov
(1844–1908)

La ci darem la mano

"Give Me Your Hand" from Don Giovanni

Wolfgang Amadeus Mozart
(1756–1791)

Theme from Piano Concerto No. 1

second movement

Peter I. Tchaikovsky

Theme from Piano Concerto No. 2

Sergei Rachmaninov
(1873–1943)

Csárdás

celebrated Hungarian dance

V. Monti

Entry of the Gladiators

Thunder and Blazes

Julius Fučik
(1872–1916)

Maple Leaf Rag

Scott Joplin

D.C. al Fine

In a Monastery Garden

Theme

Albert W. Ketèlbey
(1875–1959)

Adios muchachos

Julio Sanders

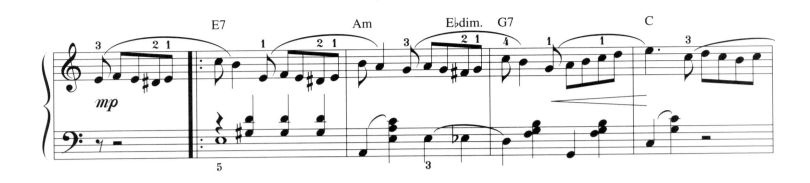

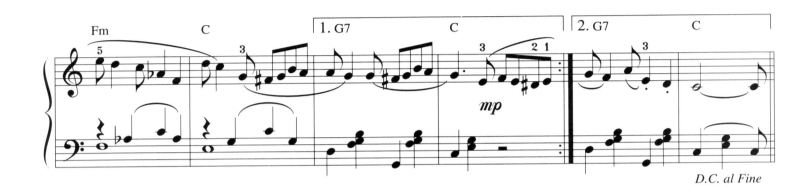

D.C. al Fine

Kashmiri Song

Laurence Hope

Amy Woodforde-Finden

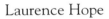

Pale hands I loved be - side the Sha - li - mar,_____ Where are you

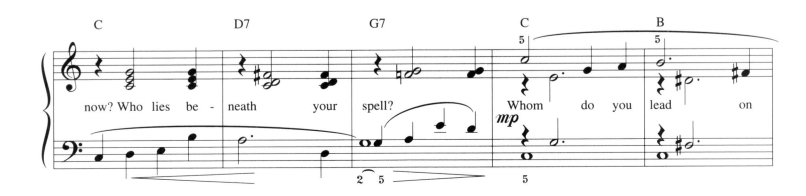

now? Who lies be - neath your spell? Whom do you lead on

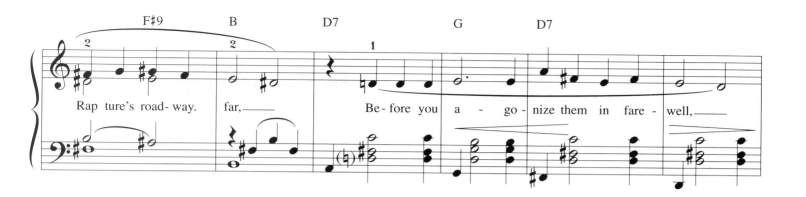

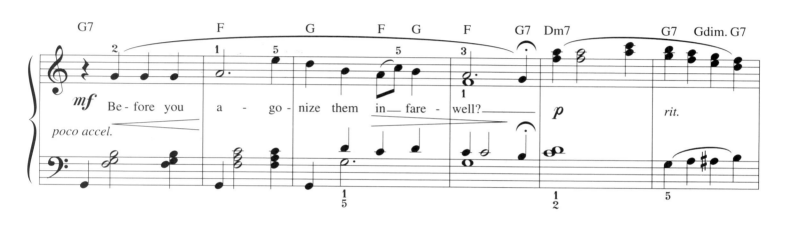

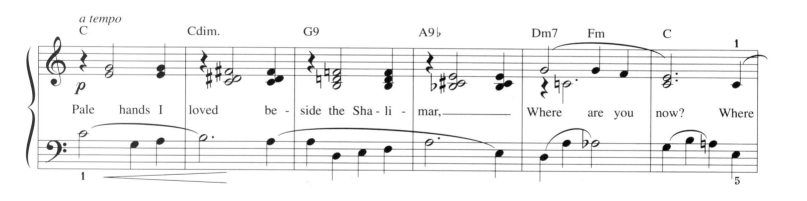

Dreams of Vienna

Wien, Wien, nur du allein

Rudolf Sieczynsky

St. Louis Blues

W. C. Handy
(1873–1958)

With a slow, heavy beat

"Colonel Bogey" March

Kenneth J. Alford

D.C. al Fine

Twelfth Street Rag

Euday L. Bowman

Gypsy Polka

Denes Agay
(1911–   )

Down by the Old Mill Stream

Tell Taylor

That's an Irish Lullaby

Too-ra-loo-ral

J. R. Shannon

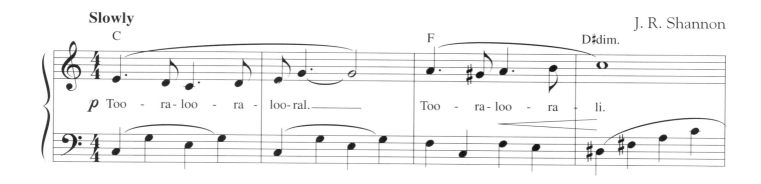

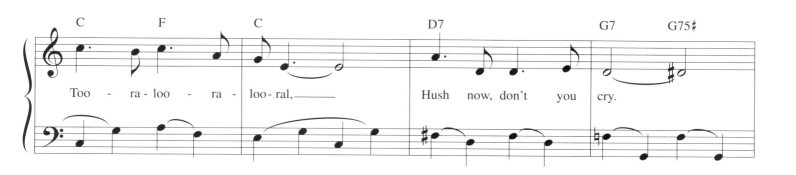

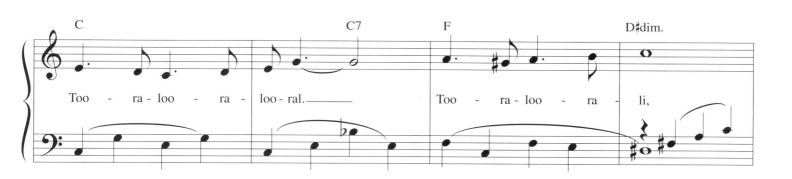

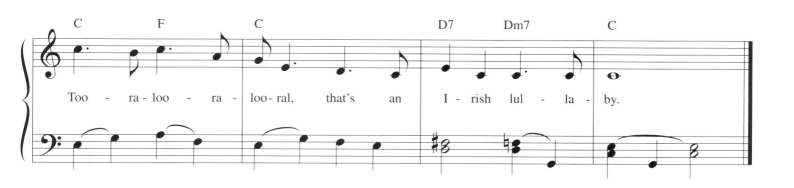

You Made Me Love You

Words by
Joe McCarthy

Music by
James V. Monaco

If You Were the Only Girl

Words by
Clifford Grey

Music by
Nat D. Ayer

For Me and My Gal

Words by
Edgar Leslie and
E. Ray Goetz

Music by
George W. Meyer

They Didn't Believe Me

Herbert Reynolds

Jerome Kern

And when I told them how won-der-ful you are,
They did-n't be-lieve me, they did-n't be-lieve me!
Your lips, your eyes, your cheeks, your hair Are in a
class be-yond com-pare, You're the love-li-est girl
that one could see! And when I tell them,

Roses of Picardy

Words by
Fred E. Weatherly

Music by
Haydn Wood